CALL ME MRS.

CALL ME MRS.

by

Stanley & Janice Berenstain

1961
The Macmillan Company
New York

First Printing

The Macmillan Company, New York
Brett-Macmillan Ltd., Galt, Ontario

Printed in the United States of America

Library of Congress catalog card number: 61-10345

CALL ME MRS.

Today's Woman

Today's woman concentrates on fundamental rather than surface values.

She knows, for example, that whichever way the fashion wind blows a good foundation garment is basic to silhouette control.

Today's woman is quick to adopt new techniques—her enthusiastic acceptance of the spray dispenser, for example, has transformed the messy make-up chore into a veritable ballet.

ALL RIGHT! WHO SWITCHED THE LABELS?

B.

9

And *of course* she is alert to new and interesting fashion developments. She does not, however, slavishly follow the dictates of the salons. When a new look comes along, she always asks herself the same stern question:

"IS IT RIGHT FOR ME?"

11

OLD SCHOOL CHUM

*"Aren't these electric eye doors
just marvelous?"*

"Yeah, that's him!"

"With ten thousand pounds of meat cut and
wrapped, why do you have to
ring the little bell?"

"HELLO, THERE!"

"Tell you what—while I wait here, why don't
you mosey around and pick up
these few things."

"Let's see, now—Monday, Tuesday,
Wednesday, Thursday . . ."

"Oh, goody! I think this is going to give
me enough trading stamps to get that
hurricane lamp I've been saving for."

HOWLER

SANG FROID

⑤

⑥

⑦

⑧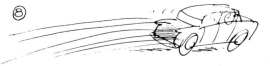

⑨

MATERNITY HOSPITAL

23

"Will you stop staring at that damn mirror
and feed the baby!"

"*Thankoo oodles for the wuvy dovey didey bag.*
I hope oo tan wead my Daddyums wighting.
Wuv,
Carole Ann."

"They're out of the labor room and
into anesthetics."

"Turn her over on her stomach."

The Responsible Woman

No longer content to follow her husband's political lead, today's woman is a powerful new force in politics—searching, seeking, questioning . . .

29

Today's woman knows that while charity begins at home, it does not end there, and she is always ready to "shake the can for sweet charity."

She understands the importance of education and works tirelessly for better schools.

Remembering always that all her activities stem from one powerful motivating force—a deep concern for the well being of her family.

BEST SELLER

36

WHAT IS YOUR G.Q.? (Glamour Quotient)
A Test for Wives

1. Which of the following corresponds most closely to your husband's conversation pattern at breakfast?
   A. Reaches his cup around in front of his paper and grunts for his second cup of coffee.
   B. Puts his paper down and says, "You know something . . . —oh, the hell with it," and resumes reading paper.
   C. Engages you in an animated discussion of vital issues of the day (whether the Yankees will take it again this year; will Tracy foil Fly Face, etc.).
2. Which of the following most nearly describes your husband's behavior pattern when he leaves for work in the morning?
   A. Kisses you good-bye somewhere on the face.
   B. Stoops to kiss you good-bye. Misses.
   C. Asks for more of that good coffee, then makes a quick get-away when your back is turned.
3. Which of the following corresponds most closely to your husband's behavior pattern when accompanying you into a building?
   A. Opens the door for you, takes your elbow if there is a step, and follows you into the building.
   B. Precedes you through door, but holds it open until you get through.
   C. Precedes you through door, making no effort to prevent it from swinging back heavily and smacking you right square in the face.

4. Which of the following most accurately reflects your husband's attitude about "special days"?
   A. Three days after event says, "Goddamn! Last Tuesday was your birthday, wasn't it, or was it our anniversary . . . it wasn't Valentine's Day? . . . don't tell me, now . . ."
   B. Gives you a big wet kiss and says how lucky he is to have a wife who doesn't make a big fuss about birthdays and anniversaries and such.
   C. Is always Johnny-on-the-spot with something black and lacy.
5. Which of the following statements most accurately reflects your husband's late night behavior pattern?
   A. Watches the Late Show *and* the Late-Late Show, occasionally sleeping all night in front of the TV in his "Bodytour" chair.
   B. Comes to bed after the Late Show. (Except on those nights when the Late-Late Show is presenting an old Alice Faye, Betty Grable, or Dorothy Lamour movie.)
   C. R-R-R-R-uff!

. . . .

CORRECT ANSWERS

1. C, 2. A, 3. A, 4. C, 5. C

. . . .

YOUR G.Q.

Five correct answers . .	long, low whistle
Four correct answers . .	OK
Three correct answers . .	OK from a distance
Less than three	*Do* something!

"Let's see, now, a dollar-and-a-quarter plus a
ten cent tip is one-thirty-five which
divided by four comes to . . ."

"The first one that giggles buys lunch."

"Let's take off our wedding rings and
live dangerously . . ."

"*I know we've been friends a long time,
Madge . . .*"

"I told you we shouldn't leave Rock Hudson
for last. It makes it so hard to go home."

"What **didn't** *we do* is a better question!"

DRIVING LESSON

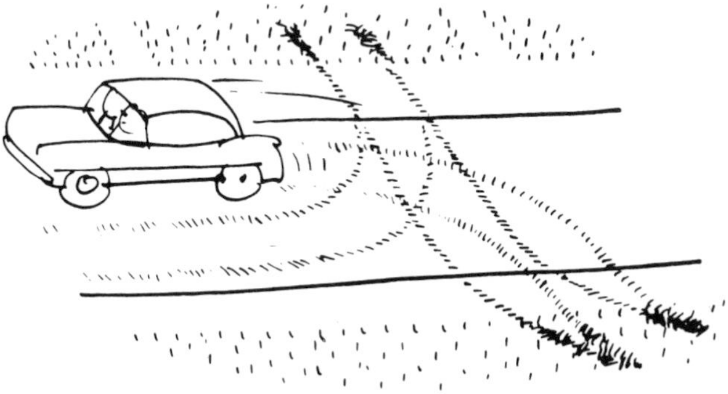

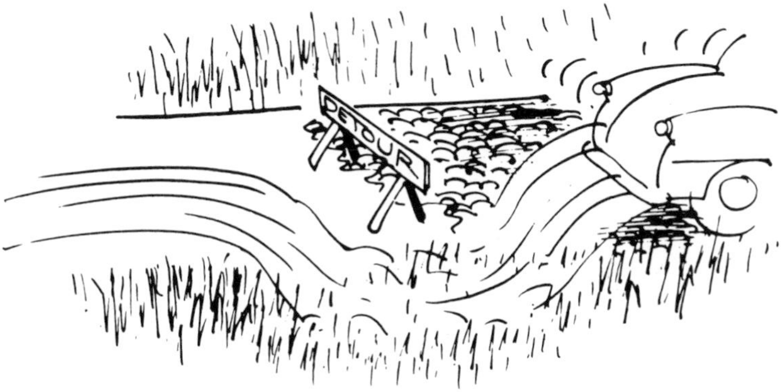
DETOUR

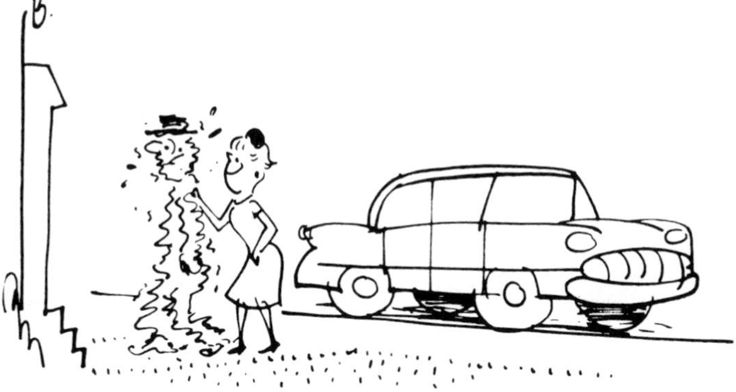
B.

BILL'S MOTHER
IS ALL RIGHT··
WE GET ALONG
BEAUTIFULLY··
REALLY···

OF COURSE, SHE
DOTES ON BILL- BUT
THEN SHE'S HIS MOTHER
... AND SHE <u>DOES</u> TEND
TO "DROP IN" A LITTLE
OFTEN ...

AND I COULD <u>CERTAINLY</u> DO WITHOUT THAT MISERABLE CHICKEN SOUP SHE KEEPS BRINGING OVER- "IT'S BILL'S <u>FAVORITE</u>, YOU KNOW"..

NOT TO <u>MENTION</u> THOSE
CRUMMY LITTLE REMARKS ABOUT
HOW <u>TWO</u> CHILDREN AREN'T
REALLY A <u>FAMILY</u> · · ·

AND AS FOR HER
ROTTEN LITTLE BITS OF
<u>ADVICE</u> ON BRINGING
UP <u>CHILDREN</u> · · ·

"*Now, let me handle this!*"

"Of course, what I'm really interested in,
Mr. Hickey, is a really old
cherry drop-leaf table."

"Well, old cherry drop-leafs are pretty
scarce. Might just have one out in the shed,
though. . . . I can let you have it
for 250 dollars as is."

"OH, *IT'S* BEAUTIFUL!"

"Did you see those black chairs back there?
Do you have any idea what they were?"

HAVE YOU HEARD THE ONE ABOUT...

House Gorgeous

One of the most striking developments of recent years is the way today's woman has taken hold in the area of home decoration.

No longer satisfied with look-alike decor, the modern homemaker goes to great lengths to—

Obtain that special piece,

··· THEN HE SAID, "WELL, OLD CHERRY DROP LEAFS ARE PRETTY SCARCE. MIGHT JUST HAVE ONE OUT IN THE SHED, THOUGH ··· I CAN LET YOU HAVE IT FOR 250 DOLLARS AS IS."

—achieve the special effect.

Recognizing the importance of this trend we present—A Collection of Significant Rooms with Personal Comments by Their Creators

MIX

WHAT IS YOUR J.Q.? (Jealousy Quotient)
A Test for Wives

1. Your husband is making a fool of himself with a young thing at a party.... Would you—
   A. Tell in a loud, clear voice what happened the last time he tried to do the Cha-Cha and how he's had to sleep on a bed board ever since.
   B. Bring out pictures of the children and pass them around.
   C. Creep up behind him while he's spinning his line and tie his shoe laces together.
2. You and your husband see a movie starring Marilyn Monroe, Brigitte Bardot, or Gina Lollobrigida. As you are leaving he says, "You know, she's quite a fine little actress." ... Do you—
   A. Laugh explosively.
   B. Snort derisively.
   C. Smile inwardly.
3. Your husband comes home from the office party with lipstick on his nose.... Would you—
   A. Slam the door on it.
   B. Check your state's community property laws.
   C. Show the true Christmas spirit and give him a chance to explain.
4. What do you say when hubby tells you that the reason he buys *Plaything, Ogle,* and *Voyeur* is so he can read the articles and stories?
   A. *"HA!"*
   B. "Pshhh!"
   C. "Su-u-ure you do!"

. . . .

CORRECT ANSWERS

1. A, 2. C, 3. C, 4. C

. . . .

YOUR J.Q.

Four correct answers . . not a jealous bone in your body

Three correct answers . maybe a couple jealous bones in your body

Two correct answers . . hello, there, Green-eyes!

Less than two . . . . see a doctor!

HE WAS SUCH A
NICE YOUNG
MAN.

ALL THE COMFORTS OF HOME

"What's the matter with Mommy?"

"CAN I HELP IT IF I'M COMPASSIONATE?"

"Gee, was I that bad?"

"*DADDY! COME QUICK!*"

DOUBLE-TAKE

Weight Watching

Today's woman *talks* a lot about diet-
ing and weight control, but she rarely
does anything about it until she is
brought up short by some such factor
as—

last year's bathing suit,

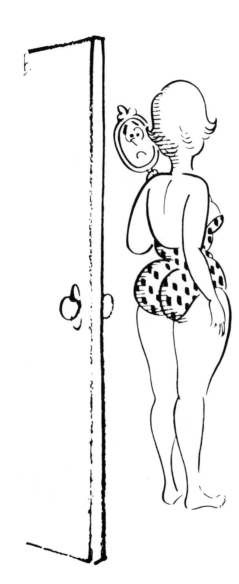

friend hubby's reaction to her new
toreador pants,

or the picture of "Mommy" Junior
brings home from nursery school.

The approach to weight control varies with the individual woman.

Some, alert to the danger of drastic methods, prefer to cut down gradually.

The "bulking" type of reducing agent that is taken before meals with a couple of glasses of warm water "does the job" for many dietees.

Some weight watchers find that low calorie cakes and candies are just the thing to spice up the dull diet day.

Still others are drawn to the world famous Six Day Crash Diet.

FIRST DAY

1 WHEAT GERM
   WAFER
1 CUP YOGHURT
1 SMALL GLASS
   SOURKRAUT
   JUICE

SECOND DAY

1 BOILED EGG
2½ CUP CHOPPED
    CABBAGE
½ GRAPEFRUIT

THIRD DAY

1 TBLSP. SUNFLOWER
    SEEDS.
½ SLI. GLUTEN BREAD
½ CUP SKIM MILK

FOURTH DAY

1 TBLSP. LIVER
EXTRACT
$\frac{1}{2}$ CUP COTTAGE
CHEESE
2 RYE WAFERS

FIFTH DAY

1 OUNCE BREWER'S
YEAST
3 RAW OYSTERS
$\frac{1}{2}$ CUP OF WHEY

But whichever approach she chooses, her objective is the same—to retain health and vigor so as better to carry out her responsibilities as wife and mother.

GIFT FROM THE SEA

①

②

③

④

⑤

"What should I sign you up for on this year's Fair—booth building, barker, or clean-up squad?"

"Of course, we didn't start any actual work
—we figured that with tomorrow being
Saturday and most of the husbands
being home . . ."

"... So I say to her, 'Look, I'm willing
to go along with the Steering Committee
on the spaghetti supper but as a
member of the Executive Board ...'"

"*I DON'T KNOW WHAT WE'D DO WITHOUT OUR WONDERFUL SCHOOL CUSTODIAN!*"

"THREE SPONGES FOR A DIME,
NINE FOR A QUARTER!"

"Madame Chairman, as Principal of Grimly
School, I want to say that I accept
this magnificent glockenspiel purchased with
funds raised by you lovely ladies
of the P.T.A. Fair Committee . . ."

ORGY

The Woman Driver

Present research reveals that many
widely held assumptions about the
woman driver are false.

The service industry reports, for example, that when properly motivated the woman driver is highly "maintenance minded."

Not only does she rarely run out of gas . . .

. . . but she is much more alert to the efficacy of having her oil and water checked periodically.

Add the fact that surveys show the woman driver

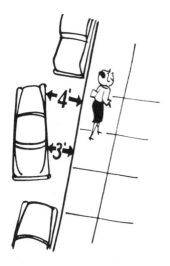

is easier on
white-wall
tires,

gets fewer
tickets,

has fewer accidents,

and is calmer in a crisis,

and the true picture of
the woman driver as she is
today begins to emerge.

Nor should the woman driver be labeled incompetent just because she refuses to use the prescribed hand signals.

A recent study reveals that her system of signals, while arcane, is far from meaningless.

A Glossary of the Signals
Commonly Used by the Woman Driver

" I JUST DON'T TRUST THESE
DOPEY TURN SIGNALS."

" HOLD YOUR HORSES! I'M
FIXING MY MAKE UP. "

" JUST HAD MY NAILS DONE."

" TRYING TO THROW AWAY
JUNIOR'S GUM."

"DROPPED MY KEYS."

" DROPPED MY KEYS AND THEY WENT UNDER THE SEAT. "

" BE RIGHT BACK. MAILING A LETTER."

" LEFT TURN, RIGHT TURN, OR SUDDEN STOP. "

TASTEMAKER

③

④

OPTOMETRIS

B.

129

TODAY'S MOTHER

Today's mother is **foresighted**

131

Today's mother is **informed**

Today's mother is **serene**

Today's mother is **objective**

WHAT IS YOUR T.Q.? (Tolerance Quotient)
A Test for Wives

1. You discover that hubby has been pasting the contents of *Playboy* into *U.S. News and World Report* covers. What would be your response?
   A. *"AHA!"*
   B. "Hmmmmm."
   C. "Heh, heh, heh."

2. You're getting the coat hubby wears to his Thursday bowling league ready for the cleaners and you find a stub from a burlesque theater. Would you—
   A. Take up bowling.
   B. Ask him the meaning of that thing he keeps shouting in his sleep—"taken off," or "tape it off," or "take it off," you're not sure which.
   C. Tell his mother on him.

3. Your husband calls just as you are putting a tuna fish salad into the fridge and announces that he's bringing three important buyers home for dinner. Would you—
   A. Go into shock.
   B. Scream, "In a pig's eye, you are!" loud enough into the mouthpiece for the three important buyers to hear.
   C. Hang up and open a couple more cans of tuna fish.

4. Your husband announces that he has blown your automatic dishwasher money on a nifty little outboard motor. Would you—

A. Call up the bank and tell them to stop payment on the check.

B. Call up your mother and tell her to get your room ready.

C. Call up your lawyer and tell him to get in touch with your husband's lawyer.

. . . .

CORRECT ANSWERS
1. C, 2. C, 3. C, 4. A

. . . .

YOUR T.Q.

Four correct answers . . highly tolerant
Three correct answers . moderately tolerant
Two correct answers . moderately intolerant
Less than two . . . . see a doctor!

"It came with the storm windows I
called BIgelow 4-6000 about."

"A *mobile* what?"

"Drip proof . . ."

"A man was selling them door to door."

144

"Let's see, now, with the seventeen-sixty-two
I won and the thirty-eight cents you won,
that puts us ahead eighteen dollars
for the evening."

A MOTHER'S TEARS

I JUST CAN'T
HELP IT. HE SEEMED
SO TINY, WAVING
GOOD-BYE.

TWO IS A
LITTLE YOUNG
FOR OVERNIGHT
CAMP · ·

AND LAPLAND
SEEMS SO FAR

BUT HE *IS*
A *MATURE* TWO · ·

AND MUKLUK
IS A PERFECTLY
MARVELOUS
CAMP -

EACH CHILD HAS HIS OWN REINDEER.

*"Now, Sweetie, I understand that you are
proud of your rock collection and
that you want to put it where people
can see it, but . . ."*

"Sarah Jane's Daddy's getting transferred
and she can't take her goldfish."

"A trade may be a trade, Tommy,
but that microscope . . ."

"Sure. It's a hunk of bread I was letting
get mouldy for school."

"You can't find your praying-WHAT?"

"It's OK. The mother eats them."

"Go ahead, tell me what a hard day you had
at the office. . . . I dare you!"